Pfizer Roerig

HEALTHY HEART
C·U·I·S·I·N·E

PREFACE

WHAT IS THE PFIZER/ROERIG HEALTHY HEART CUISINE PROGRAM?

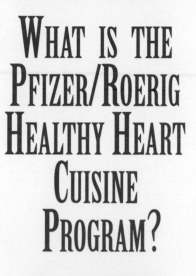

Last July, we at Pfizer/Roerig—with the endorsement of the Citizens For Public Action On Blood Pressure and Cholesterol, Inc.—invited physicians across the country to send us their favorite *heart-healthy* recipes. The response was overwhelming. Recipes were received from places as diverse as Juneau, Alaska and New Orleans, Louisiana!

A panel of nutritionists, food experts, and physicians selected what they thought to be the best recipes from the hundreds received. Among the members was the noted Antonio M. Gotto, Jr, MD, DPhil, Chairman of Medicine at Baylor College of Medicine, and Chief of Internal Medicine Service, The Methodist Hospital, Houston, Texas.

The recipes chosen were kitchen-tested and our experts were asked to make final selections based on several factors, including levels of sodium and fat, caloric and cholesterol content, ease of preparation, and—last but certainly not least—taste appeal.

The ten entries deemed best by our experts were served at the "Heart & Soul" reception during the American Academy of Family Physicians Conference in San Diego, California.

Over 3,000 physicians voted at this event for their three favorite recipes. These **"Blue Ribbon"** winners were Chicken with Toma-to–Basil Sauce (page 33), Barbecued Salmon Chardonnay (page 39) and Aloha Chicken (page 46). We'd like to congratulate the winners and thank all the contributors.

We hope you enjoy these dishes and use them to start or continue on the road to heart-healthy eating!

CONTENTS

SIDE DISHES

DESSERTS

INTRODUCTION

Lynne W. Scott, MA, RD/LD
Assistant Professor, Department of Medicine
Director, Diet Modification Clinic
Baylor College of Medicine
Houston, Texas

People often ask if diet plays a role in reducing risk of heart disease. The answer is a resounding—YES! There is a powerful link between what a person eats and two of the primary risk factors for heart disease—high blood pressure and high blood cholesterol. Both the amount and the type of food eaten are important in the control of these risk factors.

The recipes in this cookbook can be used as part of an eating plan to help control blood pressure and blood cholesterol. It is important to select other foods as well as these recipes carefully since it is the total diet, not a single food or particular dish, that helps reduce the risk of heart disease.

CONTROLLING·BLOOD·PRESSURE

What you eat can help you lower blood pressure when you do one or all of the following:

- ❤ Restrict salt and sodium
- ❤ Lose excess weight
- ❤ Limit alcoholic beverages

RESTRICT SALT AND SODIUM

Salt, which is 40% sodium and 60% chloride, is a major source of sodium in the diet. The amount of sodium in foods is reported in milligrams (mg) per serving. To determine how much sodium you are consuming, just add up the milligrams of sodium in each food you eat. You may be surprised at the amount of sodium in some foods. For example, a ham and cheese sandwich contains about 1,575 mg of sodium. If your physician has recommended that you limit your sodium intake to 2,000 mg per day, the sandwich provides more than three fourths of your total for the day.

Americans love salty foods. In fact, we each typically consume from 4,000 to 5,800 mg of sodium per day. Yet, people are not born with a taste for salt: it is learned. Remember, it usually takes about a month of eating foods with less salt or sodium to decrease your desire for it.

The most common sources of sodium in the American diet are:

- ♥ Processed foods (about 67 percent)
- ♥ Salt added during preparation— whether at home or in a restaurant— and at the table (about 18 percent)
- ♥ Natural food and water (about 15 percent)

Most processed foods, including many convenience foods, are high in sodium because of the salt or sodium compounds used for flavor and for preservation. Examples of these foods are shown below:

FOODS HIGH IN SODIUM

Anchovies	Mustard
Bacon	Nuts & seeds, salted*
Barbecue sauce	Olives
Bologna	Pastrami
Buttermilk	Pepperoni
Celery salt	Pickles*
Cereal, ready-to-eat*	Pizza
Cheese*	Salami
Chips*	Sauerkraut
Crackers*	Sausage
Cured meats	Soup*
Frankfurters	Soy sauce*
Ham	Steak sauce
Ketchup*	Wieners
Kosher processed meats	Worcestershire sauce
Meat, canned or frozen in sauce	

*Unsalted or low-sodium varieties are available.

Avoid food products listing salt or sodium as one of the first ingredients. Watch food labels for other compounds containing sodium, such as monosodium glutamate and disodium phosphate.

Obviously, one of the areas in which you have the most direct control over the amount of sodium consumed is in food preparation. Salting any food, whether during cooking or at the table, increases its sodium content. Adding more pepper, garlic, onion, lemon, or a combination of these foods helps replace the taste of salt. Since herbs and spices are very low in sodium, they can be used freely to add flavor to foods. Remember that any seasoning with "salt" in the name is high in sodium. However, garlic salt and celery salt can be replaced by garlic powder and onion powder. Most commercially prepared mixed seasonings, such as those for fajitas, meatloaf, and tacos, are very high in sodium, because salt is their primary ingredient.

The recipes in this cookbook contain very little or no salt. A small amount of salt is used in some of the recipes when other ingredients are very low in sodium.

Salt substitutes (usually potassium chloride) give a "salty" flavor when used in small amounts. It is best to add a salt substitute to food after it is cooked since heating can sometimes make the salt substitute taste bitter. Be sure to check with your physician before using a salt substitute. "Lite" salt is part real salt and part salt substitute. It is not recommended since it does add sodium to food.

Both animal and plant foods naturally contain some sodium. However, foods that are not processed and to which sodium or sodium-containing compounds have not been added are very low in sodium. Here are the approximate sodium levels in unprocessed foods:

Meat, poultry, or fish—*25 mg per oz*

Skim or low-fat milk—*120 mg per cup*

Rice or pasta cooked—*5 mg per cup*

Vegetables, fresh or frozen—*5 to 25 mg per half cup*

Fruit—*2 mg per piece*

The sodium content of water can vary widely according to the area. Check with your local health department to learn the level of sodium in your water. If your water supply is high in sodium, you may need to use distilled water or sodium-free bottled water for drinking and cooking. Remember that water softeners can add sodium to the water.

Weight Control

Obesity, which affects an estimated one out of four American adults, contributes to high blood pressure and is an important risk factor for heart disease. Initial weight loss is much easier to accomplish than keeping excess pounds off permanently. Research suggests that "yo-yo" dieting

(cycles of losing and regaining weight) may contribute to increased overall death rates and increased rates of illness and death from heart disease.

Losing excess weight usually helps lower high blood pressure and decrease levels of total cholesterol and triglyceride while increasing the level of HDL cholesterol (good cholesterol). Weight reduction results from consuming fewer calories and regularly engaging in physical activity. Decreasing your intake of fat, such as that found in fried food, fatty meat, and rich desserts, helps decrease your calories. Fat contains more than twice as many calories as protein or carbohydrate. Use the *Substitutions List* on page 6 to decrease the fat in your own recipes.

Alcohol

Alcohol increases blood pressure, blood triglyceride level, and body weight in some people. To help control blood pressure and body weight, it is recommended that alcohol be consumed only in moderation or not at all. People with a very high level of triglyceride should avoid alcohol.

CONTROLLING·BLOOD·CHOLESTEROL

What you eat affects the levels of total cholesterol, LDL cholesterol (bad cholesterol), and triglyceride in your blood. Health experts recommend that adults and healthy children two years of age and older follow an eating plan:

- ❤ Low in saturated fat
- ❤ Low in dietary cholesterol
- ❤ Containing enough calories to achieve and maintain desirable body weight

The recommended pattern of nutrient intake is that fat provide an average of no more than 30% of calories, saturated fat provide less than 10% of calories and that cholesterol intake be less than 300 mg per day.

Many of the foods we eat contain fat. Fat occurs naturally (milk, meat, poultry, and fish), is added in processing (sausage, luncheon meat, cakes, cookies, and candy), or can be added in cooking or at the table (oil and margarine).

The most important step in a cholesterol-lowering eating plan is to decrease your intake of saturated fat. Animal foods—meat fat, poultry skin, and the fat in dairy products (butter, cream, ice cream, cheese, and whole milk)—are the main sources of saturated fat in the diet. Some plant products, such as tropical oils (coconut, palm kernel, and palm oil) and cocoa butter (the fat in chocolate), also contain saturated fat. The easiest way to decrease your saturated fat intake is to reduce the total fat in your diet. Use of "low-fat" or "fat-free" foods can help decrease the amount of fat and saturated fat you eat. Foods high in saturated fat are not used as ingredients in the recipes in this cookbook.

Unsaturated fat is polyunsaturated or monounsaturated. Polyunsaturated fat is found in such vegetable oils as sunflower, safflower, corn, and soybean oils, and products made from them, such as margarine and salad dressings. Sources of monounsaturated fat are oils (olive, canola, peanut, and partially hydrogenated soybean), avocado, and nuts (especially almonds, pecans, and macadamia nuts). Recipes in this cookbook that have fat as an ingredient use a polyunsaturated or a monounsaturated oil or margarine.

Cholesterol is found only in animal foods–egg yolk, dairy products, meat, poultry, and fish. An eating pattern containing a maximum of 6 oz of cooked meat, poultry, and fish per day and 3 egg yolks per week and including low-fat and fat-free dairy products will average less than 300 mg of cholesterol per day. A cholesterol-lowering eating pattern is based as much on "adding in" as on "cutting out". It is recommended that as fat is decreased, foods high in complex carbohydrates (such as bread, cereal, rice, pasta, dry beans, and vegetables) and fruit be increased. Fruits and complex carbohydrate foods provide vitamins, minerals, and fiber.

SELECTING INGREDIENTS

The first step in preparing the recipes in the *Healthy Heart Cuisine Cookbook* is to find the right ingredients—no small task since there are about 30,000 items in most supermarkets from which to choose.

The tables on pages 6 and 7, *Substitu-*

tions for Low-Fat, Low-Sodium Recipes and *Food Facts to Make Shopping and Cooking Easier,* will help you maintain a heart-healthy diet.

RECIPE SELECTION

When physicians from across the country sent their favorite recipes to Pfizer/Roerig for the *Healthy Heart Cuisine Cookbook,* a computerized nutrient analysis was done to determine the number of calories and the amount of fat, saturated fat, cholesterol, and sodium per serving of each recipe. This computer analysis showed that some of the recipes were higher in fat and/or sodium than could be recommended. To be able to include these recipes in the collection, it was necessary to change some of the ingredients. Foods low in fat and/or sodium from the Substitutions Table on page 6 were used, or in a few recipes the serving size was decreased. The new recipes were then re-analyzed and those analyses are printed in this cookbook. Each recipe was prepared by a professional recipe tester, either just as received or according to the low-fat, low-sodium variation.

The recipes in this cookbook are low in calories, total fat, saturated fat, cholesterol, and sodium. They have been selected from hundreds of recipes submitted from physicians living in all 50 states.

Recipe Analyses by:

Lynne W. Scott, MA, RD/LD

Assistant Professor, Department of Medicine

Director, Diet Modification Clinic,

Baylor College of Medicine, Houston, Texas

Substitutions for Low-Fat, Low-Sodium Recipes

When the recipe calls for:	Substitute:
baking chocolate (1 square)	3 tablespoons cocoa plus 1 tablespoon tub margarine or 1 teaspoon oil
baking powder (1 teaspoon)	1 teaspoon baking soda plus ½ teaspoon cream of tartar or 3 teaspoons low-sodium baking powder
broth	unsalted broth or salt-free bouillon cubes
butter	tub margarine (use same amount)
buttermilk (1 cup)	1 cup minus 1 tablespoon skim, ½% lowfat, or 1% low-fat milk plus 1 tablespoon vinegar
cheese	low-fat or nonfat cheese and reduced-sodium or no-salt-added cheeses are available
coconut	coconut extract (texture of product will be different)
cream, sour	low-fat sour cream
cream, whipping or half and half	canned evaporated skim milk (can be whipped)
creamer, nondairy	skim, ½% low-fat, or 1% low-fat milk; nonfat dry milk powder; canned evaporated skim milk
eggs (1 whole)	¼ cup egg substitute or 2 egg whites
margarine (½ cup)	½ cup unsalted margarine or ⅓ cup oil
milk	skim, ½% low-fat, or 1% low-fat milk; canned evaporated skim milk
milk, evaporated	canned evaporated skim milk
shortening or lard (½ cup)	½ cup tub margarine (unsalted varieties are available) or ⅓ cup oil
tomato juice	salt-free tomato juice

Food Facts to Make Shopping and Cooking Easier

Baking Ingredients	1 pound of all-purpose flour is 4 cups (sifted)
	1 pound of whole wheat flour is about 3 ½ cups (stirred, not sifted)
	1 pound of granulated sugar is 2 cups
	1 pound of light brown sugar is 2 ⅔ cups
Cheese	1 pound of cheese yields about 4 cups grated
Eggs	1 whole egg equals about ¼ cup
Meat, Poultry, and Fish	1 chicken (broiler) yields about 3 ½ cups of cooked meat
	1 chicken breast (2 halves) yields about 6 to 7 ounces of cooked meat
	1 pound of flaked fish is about 2 cups
	1 pound ground meat is about 2 cups
Cereals	1 ½ ounces (about 7 tablespoons) of dry oat bran yields about 1 ⅕ cups cooked
	1 ½ ounces (about ½ cup) of dry oatmeal yields about 1 ⅛ cups cooked
	1 ½ ounces (3 tablespoons) of dry bulgur yields ½ cup plus 1 tablespoon cooked
Rice	2 cups of uncooked rice yields 6 cups cooked
Pasta	1 pound (4 cups) dry macaroni yields approximately 8 cups cooked
	2 ounces (about ½ cup) dry macaroni yields about 1 cup plus 1 tablespoon cooked
	1 pound (5 cups) dry spaghetti yields approximately 10 cups cooked
Dried Beans	1 pound (1 ½ cups) kidney beans yields 9 cups cooked
	1 pound (2 ⅓ cups) lima beans yields 6 cups cooked
	1 pound (2 ⅓ cups) navy beans yields 6 cups cooked
Fruits and Vegetables	1 pound of fresh apples equals about 3 medium and yields about 3 ½ cups peeled and sliced
	1 pound of bananas is about 3 medium
	1 large lemon contains ¼ cup (2 fluid ounces) of juice, and 1 medium lemon yields about 3 tablespoons of juice and about 1 tablespoon of grated rind
	1 pound of fresh tomatoes is about 3 medium to large
	1 pound of fresh potatoes is about 3 medium, and yields about 2 ¼ cups cooked

BREAD

SPICY CORN BREAD

Nonstick spray

1 ¼ cups all-purpose flour

¾ cup white or yellow cornmeal

2 tablespoons light brown sugar

1 ½ teaspoons baking powder

½ teaspoon baking soda

½ teaspoon cayenne pepper

½ teaspoon mild chili powder

½ teaspoon salt

1 cup buttermilk

¼ cup olive oil

2 egg whites, lightly beaten

❤ ❤ ❤ ❤ ❤

1. Preheat oven to 400°F. Spray an 8 x 8-inch baking pan with nonstick spray. In a large mixing bowl, stir together all the dry ingredients. Make a well in the center.

2. In a small bowl, whisk together buttermilk, oil, and egg whites. Pour the dry ingredients into the well; stir just to combine. Pour batter into prepared pan. Bake 20 to 25 minutes until golden brown and a cake tester inserted in the center comes out clean. Serve warm or at room temperature. Cut into 16 squares.

Yield: 16 servings

Contributed by:
Dr Andre Weinberger
Washington, DC

1 SERVING CONTAINS:

Calories	Fat	Saturated Fat	Cholesterol	Sodium
104	3.7 gm	0.6 gm	0 mg	151 mg

Fruit Muffins

Paper muffin liners or
   nonstick spray
4 cups all-purpose flour
2 cups sugar
2 teaspoons baking soda
3 egg whites, lightly beaten
½ cup vegetable oil

1¼ cups mashed banana
   (about 4 medium)
1½ cups buttermilk
1 can (17 ounces) apricots, drained
   and coarsely chopped (1 cup)
1½ cups raisins
1 tablespoon oat bran

❤ ❤ ❤ ❤ ❤

1. Preheat oven to 400°F. Line 30 2½-inch muffin tins with paper liners or
   spray with nonstick spray; set aside.

2. In a large bowl, stir together flour, sugar, and baking soda. In a
   medium-size bowl, stir together egg whites, oil, banana,
   buttermilk, apricots, and raisins.

3. Make a well in the center of the dry ingredients and pour in the liquid
   ingredients, stirring just until blended; do not over mix. Spoon batter into
   prepared tins, sprinkle oat bran on top. Bake for 25 to 30 minutes or
   until a wooden pick inserted in the center of one muffin comes
   out clean.
   Yield: 30 servings

Contributed by:
Dr C.G. Wuest
Iowa City, IA

1 SERVING CONTAINS:

Calories	Fat	Saturated Fat	Cholesterol	Sodium
197	4.3 g	0.9 g	2 mg	45 mg

Zesty Tomato Bread

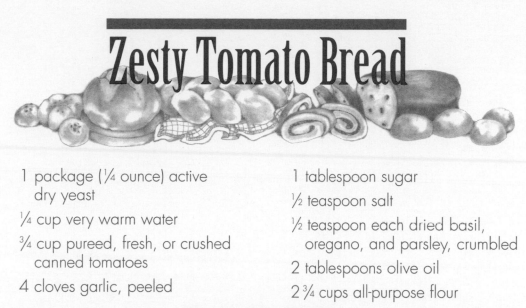

1 package (¼ ounce) active
dry yeast

¼ cup very warm water

¾ cup pureed, fresh, or crushed
canned tomatoes

4 cloves garlic, peeled

1 tablespoon sugar

½ teaspoon salt

½ teaspoon each dried basil,
oregano, and parsley, crumbled

2 tablespoons olive oil

2 ¾ cups all-purpose flour

❤   ❤   ❤   ❤   ❤

1. Dissolve yeast in water in a small bowl until creamy, about 5 minutes.

2. In the workbowl of a food processor, combine tomato, garlic, sugar, salt, basil, oregano, parsley, and olive oil and whirl until smooth. Add yeast mixture and flour, process until dough forms a ball. Transfer dough to a lightly oiled bowl, cover, and let rise in a warm spot until doubled in bulk, about 1 hour.

3. Punch down, shape into a ball on a lightly floured work surface, transfer to a baking sheet, cover and let rise until doubled in bulk, about 45 minutes.

4. Preheat oven to 350°F. Bake until bottom sounds hollow when tapped, about 40 minutes. Cool.
Yield: **10 servings**

Contributed by:
Dr Manju B. Hapke
Omaha, NE

1 SERVING CONTAINS:

Calories	Fat	Saturated Fat	Cholesterol	Sodium
165	3.1 g	0.4 g	0 mg	183 mg

Apricot Bread

1 tablespoon active dry yeast

1½ cups very warm water

3 cups bread flour

1 cup uncooked old fashioned oats

3 tablespoons firmly packed brown sugar

1 tablespoon vegetable oil

1 cup coarsely chopped dried apricots

Nonstick spray

♥ ♥ ♥ ♥ ♥

1. In the large bowl of an electric mixer, sprinkle yeast over water and let sit until creamy, about 5 minutes. Stir in remaining ingredients and mix well. Cover and let rise in a warm, draft-free spot until doubled in bulk, about 1 hour.

2. Spray two 8 x 4-inch loaf pans with nonstick spray. Scrape batter into the pans, cover and let rise until doubled in bulk, about 45 minutes.

3. Preheat oven to 350°F. Bake the loaves until they sound hollow when tapped on the bottom and a wooden pick inserted in the center comes out clean. Remove from pan and cool on a wire rack.
   Yield: 2 loaves; 12 slices per loaf (24 slices total)

Contributed by:
Dr Arlene Brown
Ruidoso, NM

1 SERVING CONTAINS:

Calories	Fat	Saturated Fat	Cholesterol	Sodium
100	1.0 g	0.1 g	0 mg	2 mg

Cranberry Muffins

Paper muffin liners
1 cup unsifted all-purpose flour
1 cup unsifted whole wheat flour
¼ cup sugar
2 teaspoons baking powder
½ teaspoon baking soda
¾ teaspoon grated orange zest

½ cup buttermilk
¼ cup orange juice
1 egg, lightly beaten
3 tablespoons vegetable oil
1 cup fresh or frozen (thawed) chopped cranberries

❤ ❤ ❤ ❤ ❤

1. Preheat oven to 350°F. Line one dozen 2½-inch muffin cups with paper muffin liners.

2. Stir together all-purpose flour, whole wheat flour, sugar, baking powder, baking soda, and orange zest in a large bowl, making a well in the center. Combine buttermilk, orange juice, egg, and oil and pour into the center, stirring until just combined. Fold in cranberries. Spoon batter into prepared muffin cups.

3. Bake 25 to 30 minutes or until a wooden pick inserted in the center of muffin comes out clean.
   Yield: 12 servings

Contributed by:
Dr Sharon Gluck
Brooklyn, NY

1 SERVING CONTAINS:

Calories	Fat	Saturated Fat	Cholesterol	Sodium
134	4.2 g	0.7 g	16 mg	114 mg

APPETIZERS

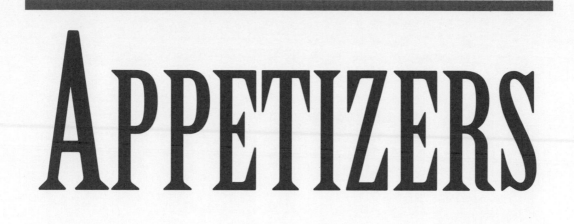

Black Bean Soup

2 tablespoons canola oil

½ cup chopped onion

1 clove garlic, peeled and crushed

1 can (16 ounces) no-salt canned tomatoes, undrained

2 cans (16 ounces each) black beans, drained and rinsed

1 can (14¾ ounces) low sodium chicken broth

½ teaspoon ground cumin

¼ cup chopped fresh tomato

2 tablespoons sliced green onion, white and green parts

❤ ❤ ❤ ❤ ❤

1. Heat oil in a medium-size saucepan set over moderate heat. Add onion and garlic, cook stirring occasionally until softened, about 5 minutes.

2. Combine canned tomatoes and 1 can of beans in a blender and puree. Add pureed mixture, remaining can of beans, chicken broth, and cumin to the saucepan and cook until heated through, about 5 minutes. Serve garnished with fresh tomato and scallion.

Yield: **8 servings**

Contributed by:
Dr Joel B. Burwell
Gulfport, MS

1 SERVING CONTAINS:

Calories	Fat	Saturated Fat	Cholesterol	Sodium
184	2.1 g	0.3 g	0 mg	358 mg

Cabbage Soup

1 medium-size head cabbage,
    cut into 2-inch pieces (9 cups)

2 large onions, diced (2 cups)

4 cloves garlic, thinly sliced

3¼ cups water

1 can (28 ounces) crushed tomatoes

1 teaspoon oregano

4 cloves

❤   ❤   ❤   ❤   ❤

1. Place cabbage, onion, garlic, and 1 cup of the water in a Dutch oven set over moderate heat. Cook until cabbage has wilted, about 10 minutes.

2. Add remaining water, tomatoes, oregano, and cloves, bring to a boil, reduce to a simmer, and cook 45 minutes.
    Yield: **8 servings**

Contributed by:
Dr George Colvin
North Woodmere, NY

1 SERVING CONTAINS:

Calories	Fat	Saturated Fat	Cholesterol	Sodium
70	0.5 g	0.1 g	0 mg	184 mg

Tortillas Con Frijoles

8 corn tortillas (8 or 9 inch)

½ cup frijoles (recipe below)

½ cup Salsa Mexicana (recipe follows)

8 green leaf lettuce leaves, shredded

3 medium-size zucchini,
   coarsely chopped

3 medium-size tomatoes,
   cored and coarsely chopped

❤   ❤   ❤   ❤   ❤

1. Preheat oven to 400°F. Place tortillas on a baking sheet and bake 5 minutes or until lightly toasted.

2. Top each tortilla with 1 tablespoon frijoles, 1 tablespoon salsa, lettuce, zucchini, and tomatoes; fold up to eat.
   Yield: 8 servings

Frijoles:

1. Soak 1 cup dried pinto beans in water overnight. Drain and rinse. Cover with fresh water, bring to a boil, reduce to a simmer, and cook until tender, about 1½ hours.

2. Drain and partially mash.

Contributed by:
*Dr Bari J. Bett
Arlington, VA*

1 SERVING CONTAINS:

Calories	Fat	Saturated Fat	Cholesterol	Sodium
117	1.5 g	0.2 g	0 mg	45 mg

Salsa Mexicana

4 medium-size tomatoes, peeled and chopped

1 small onion, minced

1 carrot, minced

1 stalk celery, minced

1 sweet red or green pepper, diced

½ to 2 jalapeno peppers, minced, or to taste

¼ to ⅓ cup chopped fresh cilantro, or to taste

2 tablespoons red wine vinegar

1 teaspoon lime juice

½ teaspoon dried oregano, crumbled

½ teaspoon garlic powder

¼ teaspoon pepper

❤ ❤ ❤ ❤ ❤

1. Combine all ingredients in a large bowl, mix well.

2. Cover and refrigerate at least 2 hours before serving.
   Yield: 3 cups

Contributed by:
Dr Bari J. Bett
Arlington, VA

1 SERVING CONTAINS:

Calories	Fat	Saturated Fat	Cholesterol	Sodium
105	0.3 g	0.1 g	0 mg	15 mg

Hearty Chicken Macaroni Soup

3 skinless chicken drumsticks

7 cups water

1 teaspoon canola oil

1 cup diced onion

1 teaspoon minced garlic

½ cup diced celery

½ cup diced carrots

¼ cup minced fresh coriander

½ teaspoon each salt substitute and sugar

¼ teaspoon pepper

1 cup uncooked macaroni

❤ ❤ ❤ ❤ ❤

1. Place chicken and water in a large saucepan. Bring to a boil, reduce to a simmer, and cook until meat falls off the bone, about 1 hour. Remove chicken from broth, dice meat.

2. Heat oil in a large skillet set over moderate heat. Add onion and garlic and cook until soft, about 7 minutes. Add the diced chicken and cook 2 minutes longer. Return onion and chicken to broth along with remaining ingredients and bring to a boil. Reduce to a simmer and cook until vegetables are tender and macaroni is cooked, about 10 minutes. Serve.

Yield: **4 servings**

Contributed by:
Dr Del P. Almeda
Rochester, MI

1 SERVING CONTAINS:

Calories	Fat	Saturated Fat	Cholesterol	Sodium
218	3.2 g	0.6 g	25 mg	46 mg

Gazpacho

5 medium-size tomatoes, peeled, seeded, and quartered

2 medium-size cucumbers, peeled, seeded, and quartered

2 medium-size sweet red or green peppers, seeded and diced

1 large onion, quartered

1 clove garlic

¼ cup red wine vinegar

2 tablespoons lemon juice

2 teaspoons chopped parsley

1 teaspoon thinly sliced chives or scallions

1 teaspoon each dried basil and tarragon, crumbled

1 teaspoon seasoned salt

½ teaspoon Worcestershire sauce

3 drops liquid red pepper seasoning

4 cups no-salt-added tomato juice

❤ ❤ ❤ ❤ ❤

1. Place all ingredients except the tomato juice in the workbowl of a food processor and whirl until pureed. Transfer to a large glass or stainless steel bowl, stir in tomato juice, and chill several hours or overnight.

2. Serve chilled.
   Yield: 8 servings

Contributed by:
Dr Robert Ebersole
Archbold, OH

1 SERVING CONTAINS:

Calories	Fat	Saturated Fat	Cholesterol	Sodium
59	0.5 g	0.1 g	0.0 mg	196 mg

ENTREES

Eggplant Parmesan

1 large eggplant, peeled and sliced ¼-inch thick (1 ¼ pounds)

3 egg whites, lightly beaten with 1 tablespoon water

1 cup plain dry bread crumbs

Nonstick spray

3 cans (8 ounces each) no-salt-added tomato sauce

1 ½ teaspoons dried oregano

⅓ cup grated Parmesan cheese

4 ounces shredded, part-skim mozzarella cheese (1 cup)

❤ ❤ ❤ ❤ ❤

1. Preheat oven to 350°F. Dip eggplant into beaten egg whites, then into bread crumbs. Spray a large nonstick skillet with cooking spray and set over moderate heat. Cook eggplant in small batches, until browned on both sides, about 4 minutes.

2. Stir tomato sauce and oregano together. Spoon 3 tablespoons of tomato sauce into an 11 x 7-inch baking pan. Place one layer of eggplant on top of sauce and sprinkle with 2 tablespoons of Parmesan cheese, ⅓ cup of mozzarella, and a scant cup of tomato sauce on top. Repeat, finishing top layer with cheese.

3. Bake 30 minutes or until bubbly.
   Yield: 4 servings

Contributed by:
*Dr Joan Curtis
Covington, LA*

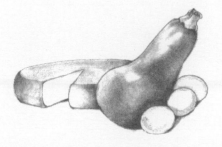

1 SERVING CONTAINS:

Calories	Fat	Saturated Fat	Cholesterol	Sodium
317	8.7 g	4.8 g	22 mg	549 mg

Penne Kalamata

¾ cup minced red onion

3 cloves garlic, minced

3 anchovy filets, minced
(1½ teaspoons)

1½ teaspoons virgin olive oil

⅔ cup oil-packed sundried
tomatoes, drained and chopped

2 medium-size fresh tomatoes,
diced

⅔ cup low-sodium chicken
broth

½ cup chopped fresh parsley

½ teaspoon dried thyme,
crumbled

¼ cup pitted Kalamata olives,
minced

1 teaspoon lemon juice

2 ounces soft goat cheese,
crumbled

½ pound penne (tubular shape
pasta), cooked in unsalted water
and drained

❤ ❤ ❤ ❤ ❤

1. Sauté onion, garlic, and anchovies in oil in a large nonstick skillet over
   low heat, until onion is soft, about 7 minutes.

2. Add sundried tomatoes, fresh tomatoes, and ⅓ cup of broth. Simmer until
   reduced by half. Stir in parsley, thyme, olives, and lemon juice.

3. In a large bowl, whisk together goat cheese and remaining broth. Add
   sauce and hot pasta, toss well.
   Yield: 4 servings

Contributed by:
Dr Omar B. Ayoub
Irwin, PA

1 SERVING CONTAINS:

Calories	Fat	Saturated Fat	Cholesterol	Sodium
339	8.2 g	2.9 g	14 mg	384 mg

Teguh's Stir-Fry Tofu

2 teaspoons olive oil

1 small onion, thinly sliced

1 clove garlic, minced

8 ounces soft tofu, sliced
   1 inch thick

1 pound small shrimp, peeled
   and deveined

1 cup bean sprouts

Pinch pepper

3 tablespoons sliced green onion

1 teaspoon ketchup

⅛ teaspoon soy sauce

3 cups cooked rice (cook in
   unsalted water)

❤ ❤ ❤ ❤ ❤

1. Heat oil in a large nonstick skillet set over moderate heat. Add onion, garlic, and tofu and cook, stirring occasionally until tofu is lightly browned, about 5 minutes. Add shrimp, beansprouts, pepper, and green onion and cook 3 minutes longer or until shrimp is cooked through. Stir in ketchup and soy sauce, and cook 30 seconds longer.

2. Serve over rice.
   Yield: 6 servings

Contributed by:
Dr Collin Teguh
San Bernardino, CA

1 SERVING CONTAINS:

Calories	Fat	Saturated Fat	Cholesterol	Sodium
232	4.8 g	0.7 g	71 mg	106 mg

29

Vegetable Chili

¼ cup olive oil

2 medium-size zucchini, diced in ½-inch pieces

2 medium-size onions, diced in ½-inch pieces

2 large sweet red peppers, diced in ¼-inch pieces

4 cloves garlic, minced

1½ pounds ripe plum tomatoes, diced in 1-inch pieces

1 can (35 ounces) Italian plum tomatoes, chopped

½ cup chopped fresh parsley

2 tablespoons chili powder (not hot Mexican type)

1 tablespoon each dried basil, oregano and ground cumin

1 teaspoon each fennel seed and pepper

1 cup each cooked kidney and garbanzo beans

½ cup chopped fresh dill

2 tablespoons lemon juice

❤ ❤ ❤ ❤ ❤

1. Cook onion, pepper, and garlic in 2 tablespoons of oil in a Dutch oven over low heat, until soft, about 7 minutes. Add remaining oil and zucchini, stir to coat.

2. Add tomatoes, parsley, and spices, simmer 30 minutes. Stir in kidney beans, garbanzo beans, dill, and lemon juice and simmer 15 minutes longer.

Yield: 8 servings

Contributed by:
Dr J. Ausfahl
Peoria, IL

1 SERVING CONTAINS:

Calories	Fat	Saturated Fat	Cholesterol	Sodium
214	8.8 g	1.1 g	0 mg	348 mg

Kara's Fabulous Red Beans and Rice

2 tablespoons olive oil

1 large onion, halved and thinly sliced

2 cloves garlic, minced

1 yellow, red, or green sweet pepper, thinly sliced

2 cans (16 ounces each) cajun-style tomatoes

1 medium-size tomato, chopped

¼ teaspoon each dried basil, oregano, and thyme, crumbled

⅛ to ½ teaspoon chili powder

Pinch cayenne pepper (optional)

2 cans (15 ounces each) reduced-sodium kidney beans

3 cups cooked white or brown rice (cook in unsalted water)

3 green onions, thinly sliced

♥ ♥ ♥ ♥ ♥

1. Heat oil in a Dutch oven set over moderate heat. Add onion and garlic, cook, stirring occasionally until onion has softened, about 7 minutes. Add sweet pepper, cook 5 minutes longer.

2. Add canned and fresh tomato, basil, oregano, thyme, chili powder, and cayenne, bring to a boil, reduce to a simmer, and cook 15 minutes for all the flavors to come together. Stir in beans and cook until heated through, about 5 minutes. Spoon over rice and garnish with green onion.

Yield: 6 servings

Contributed by:
Dr Kimberly Heffron Perkins
San Diego, CA

1 SERVING CONTAINS:

Calories	Fat	Saturated Fat	Cholesterol	Sodium
361	5.9 g	0.8 g	0 mg	255 mg

Tex-Mex Turkey

Nonstick spray

4-ounce turkey tenderloin
cut into ½-inch thick strips

¼ teaspoon each
ground cumin and pepper

1 small tomato, chopped

¼ cup chopped zucchini

2 tablespoons canned chopped
green chilies, drained

1 green onion, thinly sliced

½ teaspoon cornstarch

1 teaspoon vinegar

1 teaspoon sugar

1 corn tortilla (8-inch)

❤ ❤ ❤ ❤ ❤

1. Spray a nonstick skillet with nonstick spray. Sprinkle turkey with cumin and pepper and cook over moderate heat until cooked through, about 5 minutes. Remove.

2. Stir in tomato, zucchini, chilies, and green onion, bring to a boil. In a small bowl, stir together cornstarch, vinegar, and sugar.

3. Stir into tomato mixture, return to a boil, and cook until slightly thickened. Heat corn tortilla; spoon turkey and tomato mixture into tortilla.
   Yield: 1 serving

Contributed by:
Dr Robert W. Shreck
Las Vegas, NV

1 SERVING CONTAINS:

Calories	Fat	Saturated Fat	Cholesterol	Sodium
263	4.8 g	1.2 g	67 mg	314 mg

Chicken with Tomato-Basil Sauce

1 small yellow onion, minced

1 clove garlic, minced

1½ teaspoons safflower oil

4 boned, skinless chicken breast halves (about 1 pound)

⅛ teaspoon white pepper

2 medium-size tomatoes, peeled, seeded, and chopped

2 tablespoons balsamic vinegar

⅔ cup low-sodium chicken broth

½ cup chopped fresh basil

♥ ♥ ♥ ♥ ♥

1. Cook onion and garlic in oil in a large nonstick skillet over moderate heat. Cook, stirring occasionally until softened, about 5 minutes. Reduce heat to low, push onion mixture to the side of the pan.

2. Sprinkle chicken with pepper, add to skillet and cook until just cooked through, about 10 minutes. Remove to a serving platter.

3. Add tomato and vinegar to the pan, raise heat to high and cook, scraping up any bits that have formed on the bottom of the pan. Add broth and cook until sauce is reduced and lightly thickened. Spoon any juice from the cooked chicken breasts into the sauce, add the basil, and cook 1 minute longer. Spoon over warmed chicken and serve.

Yield: 4 servings

Contributed by:
Dr David Edwards
Bellevue, IA

1 SERVING CONTAINS:

Calories	Fat	Saturated Fat	Cholesterol	Sodium
192	5.6 g	1.2 g	66 mg	78 mg

Greek Sandwich

Nonstick spray

¼ cup chopped onion

¼ cup chopped green pepper

2 cloves garlic, minced

1 boned, skinned chicken breast half, cut into ½ inch cubes

¼ cup diced sundried tomatoes

3 ripe pitted olives, sliced

¼ teaspoon dried basil, crumbled

¼ cup crumbled feta cheese

2 medium-size pita breads, warmed

❤ ❤ ❤ ❤ ❤

1. Spray a medium-size nonstick skillet with nonstick spray and set over moderate heat. Add onion, pepper, and garlic and cook, stirring occasionally until onion has softened, about 5 minutes. Add chicken and cook until no longer pink, 4 to 5 minutes. Add tomatoes, olives, and basil; cook 1 minute.

2. Remove from heat, stir in cheese, and spoon into warmed pita breads.
Yield: 2 servings

Contributed by:
Dr Richard Thomasson
Tullahoma, TN

1 SERVING CONTAINS:

Calories	Fat	Saturated Fat	Cholesterol	Sodium
268	6.4 g	2.9 g	46 mg	501 mg

Chicken and Veggie Fajitas

2 cloves garlic, minced

1 large onion, thinly sliced

1 sweet green pepper, trimmed and cut into thin strips

1 sweet red pepper, trimmed and cut into thin strips

1 can (32 ounces) stewed tomatoes

1 tablespoon chili powder

2 teaspoons ground cumin

1 teaspoon oregano leaves, crumbled

4 boned, skinless chicken breasts, cut into ½-inch thick strips

10 flour tortillas (8-inch)

⅔ cup low-fat sour cream

Aluminum foil

❤ ❤ ❤ ❤ ❤

1. Preheat oven to 400°F.

2. In a large skillet set over moderate heat, combine garlic, onion, peppers, tomatoes, chili powder, cumin, and oregano and cook 10 minutes. Add chicken, cover, and simmer 10 minutes or until chicken is tender.

3. While chicken cooks, wrap tortillas in 3 foil packets and place in oven to heat. Spoon chicken mixture onto warm tortillas, top with low-fat sour cream and serve.

Yield: **10 servings**

Contributed by:
Dr Brian Graham
Temecula, CA

1 SERVING CONTAINS:

Calories	Fat	Saturated Fat	Cholesterol	Sodium
283	8.2 g	2.8 g	35 mg	438 mg

Summer Spaghetti

1 tablespoon olive oil

2 medium-size onions, diced

3 cloves garlic, minced

1 carrot, finely chopped

1 sweet red or green pepper, diced

½ cup diced eggplant

½ cup diced summer squash

6 plum tomatoes, chopped (about 2 cups)

¾ teaspoon dried oregano, crumbled

2 tablespoons tomato paste

4 cups cooked spinach fettuccine

❤ ❤ ❤ ❤ ❤

1. Heat oil in a large skillet set over moderate heat. Add onion and garlic and cook stirring occasionally until tender, about 7 minutes. Add carrot and pepper and cook 4 minutes longer.

2. Add eggplant and squash, stir to coat. Add tomatoes and oregano, simmer until sauce is lightly thickened and flavor has developed, about 30 minutes. Add tomato paste, if sauce needs thickening. Pour over hot pasta.
Yield: 4 servings

Contributed by:
Dr J.R. Connell
Santa Rosa, CA

1 SERVING CONTAINS:

Calories	Fat	Saturated Fat	Cholesterol	Sodium
330	6.6 g	1.1 g	53 mg	102 mg

Chicken Salad

2 teaspoons reduced-calorie
  mayonnaise

2 teaspoons plain low-fat yogurt

⅛ teaspoon curry powder

1 cooked boned, skinless
  chicken breast half,
  cut into ½-inch pieces

1 stalk celery, coarsely chopped

12 seedless green grapes, halved

3 lettuce leaves, washed and dried

2 mushrooms, thinly sliced

1 flowerette broccoli

2 slices cucumber

2 sugar snap peas

3 pecan halves

❤ ❤ ❤ ❤ ❤

1. In a small bowl, stir together mayonnaise, yogurt, and curry powder. Fold in chicken, celery, and grapes.

2. Line a plate with lettuce leaves, mushrooms, cucumber, broccoli, and snap peas, top with chicken salad and garnish with pecan halves.
   Yield: 1 serving

Contributed by:
Dr Suzanna Goodyear
Clarksburg, WV

1 SERVING CONTAINS:

Calories	Fat	Saturated Fat	Cholesterol	Sodium
274	9.3 g	1.9 g	69 mg	181 mg

Shrimp Provençale

3 tablespoons olive oil

1½ pounds large shrimp, shelled and deveined

1 pound mushrooms, sliced

2 cloves garlic, minced

3 medium-size tomatoes, coarsely chopped

¼ teaspoon salt

⅛ teaspoon pepper

2 tablespoons lemon juice

2 tablespoons chopped fresh parsley

3 cups hot cooked rice (cook in unsalted water)

♥ ♥ ♥ ♥ ♥

1. Heat 2 tablespoons of the oil in a very large skillet set over moderate heat. Add shrimp, cook, stirring frequently until shrimp is no longer pink, 3 to 4 minutes. Remove and set aside.

2. Heat remaining tablespoon oil in same skillet, add mushrooms and garlic and cook, stirring frequently until mushrooms are tender, about 5 minutes. Add tomatoes, salt, and pepper, cook 5 minutes longer. Return shrimp to the skillet and cook just until heated through. Stir in lemon juice and parsley, serve over rice.

Yield: 6 servings

Contributed by:
Dr Larry Plummer
Jacksonville, IL

1 SERVING CONTAINS:

Calories	Fat	Saturated Fat	Cholesterol	Sodium
309	8.5 g	1.3 g	161 mg	287 mg

Barbecued Salmon Chardonnay

2 tablespoons fresh lemon juice

2 tablespoons Chardonnay or other dry white wine

1 salmon fillet (1 pound), skin on

2 large cloves garlic, slivered

1 teaspoon cajun spices

❤ ❤ ❤ ❤ ❤

1. In a shallow pan, stir together lemon juice and wine. Place salmon fillet skin side up in the lemon-wine mixture and marinate ½ hour.

2. Preheat barbecue or broiler with the rack 6 inches from the heat.

3. Push the garlic slivers into the flesh of the salmon from the skinned side, sprinkle with the cajun spices, and return to the marinade, skin side up.

4. Remove fish from the marinade and place on grill, skin side down. Barbecue 6 to 8 minutes or until just done, basting every 2 minutes with the marinade, or broil 6 to 8 minutes. Cut into 4 pieces.
Yield: **4 servings**

Contributed by:
Dr Norman M. Charney
San Clemente, CA

1 SERVING CONTAINS:

Calories	Fat	Saturated Fat	Cholesterol	Sodium
179	6.7 g	1.2 g	43 mg	397 mg

Lentils and Rice (Mujadara)

2 large onions, halved and thinly
   sliced (2 cups)

2 tablespoons olive oil

1 cup uncooked lentils

4½ cups water

½ cup uncooked long-grain rice

¾ teaspoon salt

¼ teaspoon pepper

1 can (4 ounces) sliced mushrooms, drained (optional)

1 container (8 ounces) plain
   low-fat yogurt

❤ ❤ ❤ ❤ ❤

1. Sauté onions in oil in a large skillet set over moderate heat until golden
   brown, about 15 minutes.

2. Rinse and pick over lentils, add to water in a 4-quart pot and bring to a
   boil. Reduce to a simmer, cover, and cook 20 minutes.

3. Add rice, salt, pepper, and half of the cooked onions. Cover and cook
   until rice is tender, about 20 minutes. Add mushrooms (if using) and
   cook until heated through, about 2 minutes. Top with remaining onion
   and yogurt.
   Yield: 8 servings

Contributed by:
Dr William A. Bartlett
Tewksbury, MA

1 SERVING CONTAINS:

Calories	Fat	Saturated Fat	Cholesterol	Sodium
193	4.3 g	0.8 g	2 mg	420 mg

Frittata

2 tablespoons olive oil

1 jar (6 ounces)
marinated artichoke hearts,
drained and coarsely chopped

1 cup coarsely chopped mushrooms

¼ cup thinly sliced green onion

1½ cups egg substitute or
egg whites, lightly beaten

2 tablespoons white wine

½ teaspoon garlic powder

2 tablespoons grated
Parmesan cheese

❤ ❤ ❤ ❤ ❤

1. Heat olive oil in a 10-inch broiler-proof skillet set over moderate heat.
Add artichoke and mushrooms and cook, stirring occasionally until slightly
softened, about 5 minutes. Add green onion and cook 2 minutes longer.

2. In a medium-size bowl, whisk together the egg substitute or egg whites,
wine, and garlic powder. Pour over the artichoke mixture, stir just to combine, then do not stir again. Cook until egg mixture is set on the bottom and
around the edges of the pan, about 5 minutes.

3. Sprinkle with Parmesan cheese, broil until golden and set. Serve from pan
while still warm.
Yield: 5 servings

Contributed by:
Dr Donald Campbell
Rolling Hills Estates, CA

1 SERVING CONTAINS:

Calories	Fat	Saturated Fat	Cholesterol	Sodium
124	7.0 g	1.3 g	2 mg	280 mg

Chicken Sesame

¼ cup sesame seeds

¼ cup sherry

¼ cup Dijon mustard

3 tablespoons honey

1 tablespoon lemon juice

4 boned, skinless chicken
breast halves (about 1 pound)

❤ ❤ ❤ ❤ ❤

1. Preheat oven to 400°F. Place sesame seeds in a shallow pan and toast in the oven until golden, about 5 minutes. In a small bowl, stir together sesame seeds, sherry, mustard, honey, and lemon juice.

2. Place chicken in a shallow baking pan just large enough to hold chicken in a single layer. Pour sesame seed mixture over and bake 15 to 20 minutes or until chicken is cooked through, basting occasionally with the sesame mixture. Remove chicken to serving plates, spoon cooking juices over and serve.

Yield: 4 servings

Contributed by:
Dr Thomas Anderson
Slidell, LA

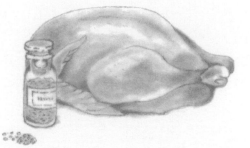

1 SERVING CONTAINS:

Calories	Fat	Saturated Fat	Cholesterol	Sodium
272	8.4 g	1.6 g	66 mg	255 mg

Chicken Delight

2 large onions, chopped
½" piece fresh ginger, pared
1 clove garlic, peeled
3 tablespoons olive oil
10 boned, skinless chicken breast
    halves (about 2 ½ pounds)
1 teaspoon ground coriander

½ teaspoon each ground cumin
    and turmeric
¼ teaspoon curry powder
⅛ to ¼ teaspoon cayenne pepper
2 large tomatoes, cored,
    quartered, and pureed
Coriander sprigs (optional)

❤ ❤ ❤ ❤ ❤

1. Combine onion, ginger, and garlic in the workbowl of a food processor; coarsely blend. Heat oil in a large skillet set over moderate heat, add onion mixture, and cook, stirring occasionally until browned, about 7 minutes. Push the onion mixture to the side of the pan, add the chicken, and cook until browned on both sides, about 5 minutes.

2. Stir in coriander, cumin, turmeric, curry, cayenne, and tomato. Reduce heat to low, cover, and cook 10 minutes or until chicken is cooked through. Garnish with fresh coriander sprigs if you wish.
Yield: 10 servings

Contributed by:
Dr Anni Thomas
Palm Harbor, FL

1 SERVING CONTAINS:

Calories	Fat	Saturated Fat	Cholesterol	Sodium
200	7.6 g	1.6 g	66 mg	65 mg

Grilled Marinated Chicken Breasts

1 tablespoon olive oil

1 teaspoon country style brown mustard

1 cup dry white wine

¼ cup chopped onion

1 clove garlic, minced

2 boned, skinless chicken breast halves
(about 1 pound)

❤ ❤ ❤ ❤ ❤

1. Whisk together oil and mustard in a shallow, non-corrosive baking pan. Stir in wine, onion, and garlic. Add chicken, cover and marinate in the refrigerator for 4 hours, turning once.

2. Preheat grill or broiler with pan 6 inches from heat source. Grill or broil until cooked through, 5 to 6 minutes per side.
Yield: 4 servings

Contributed by:
Dr Andrea Brand
Clinton, NY

1 SERVING CONTAINS:

Calories	Fat	Saturated Fat	Cholesterol	Sodium
219	6.8 g	1.5 g	66 mg	81 mg

Black Beans and Peppers

1 clove garlic, minced

1 tablespoon olive oil

1 cup chopped red, yellow, or green pepper or a mixture

½ cup chopped onion

¾ teaspoon chili powder

1 can (15 ounces) black beans, drained and rinsed

1 can (8 ounces) stewed tomatoes, chopped

1 bay leaf

⅛ to ¼ teaspoon red pepper flakes

1½ teaspoons red wine vinegar

2 cups cooked rice

❤ ❤ ❤ ❤ ❤

1. In a large skillet, sauté garlic in oil over moderately low heat for 1 minute. Add peppers and onion; increase heat to moderate, and sauté until onion has wilted and peppers are slightly softened, about 5 minutes.

2. Stir in chili powder, beans, tomatoes, bay leaf, and pepper flakes. Bring to a simmer, cover, and cook until lightly thickened, about 15 minutes. Add vinegar, cook 2 minutes longer. Remove bay leaf and serve over hot rice.

Yield: 3 servings

Contributed by:
Dr Jane Simenson
Cape Coral, FL

1 SERVING CONTAINS:

Calories	Fat	Saturated Fat	Cholesterol	Sodium
490	7.8 g	1.3 g	0 mg	537 mg

Aloha Chicken

1 can (8¼ ounces) crushed
pineapple in unsweetened juice

2 tablespoons honey

2 tablespoons commercial barbecue sauce,
preferably low sodium

6 boned, skinless chicken breast halves
(about 1½ pounds)

❤ ❤ ❤ ❤ ❤

1. In a medium-size bowl, combine pineapple and its juice, honey, and
barbecue sauce.

2. Heat an outdoor grill or preheat a broiler with the pan 6 inches from the
heat. Grill or broil chicken breasts 5 minutes per side or until thoroughly
cooked, basting every 2 minutes with sauce.

Yield: 6 servings

Contributed by:
Dr Shirley Lockie
Pearl City, HI

1 SERVING CONTAINS:

Calories	Fat	Saturated Fat	Cholesterol	Sodium
190	3.5 g	1.0 g	66 mg	104 mg

SIDE DISHES

Yogurt Mashed Potatoes

2 pounds white new potatoes, scrubbed
and quartered, unpeeled

5 cloves garlic, peeled

¼ teaspoon salt

1 container (8 ounces) plain low-fat yogurt

¼ to ½ teaspoon ground black pepper

♥ ♥ ♥ ♥ ♥

1. Combine potatoes, garlic, and salt in a large saucepan with water to
cover. Bring to a boil over moderate heat and cook until potatoes are fork
tender, about 20 minutes. Drain, reserving ⅓ cup of the cooking liquid.

2. In a large bowl, mash potatoes, garlic, and yogurt, adding enough of the
reserved potato cooking liquid to make the potatoes creamy. Add pepper
to taste.

Yield: **8 servings**

Contributed by:
Dr Sharon Gluck
Brooklyn, NY

1 SERVING CONTAINS:

Calories	Fat	Saturated Fat	Cholesterol	Sodium
143	0.6 g	0.3 g	2 mg	96 mg

Italian Tossed Green Salad

½ cup shredded red cabbage

2 ripe plum tomatoes, cut into wedges

1 carrot, shredded

1 medium zucchini, thinly sliced

1 sweet red bell pepper, cut into thin rings

1 package creamy Italian nonfat dressing mix

½ cup water

¼ cup red wine vinegar

1 head iceberg lettuce, torn into small pieces

❤ ❤ ❤ ❤ ❤

1. Combine cabbage, tomatoes, carrot, zucchini, and bell pepper in a large bowl. Whisk together dressing, water, and vinegar; pour over salad ingredients. Toss to combine, cover, and refrigerate 1 hour for flavors to blend.

2. Add lettuce, toss again, and serve.
   Yield: 10 servings

Contributed by:
Dr Brian Graham
Temecula, CA

1 SERVING CONTAINS:

Calories	Fat	Saturated Fat	Cholesterol	Sodium
26	0.5 g	0.2 g	3 mg	42 mg

Pasta a la Savannah

3 cups uncooked pasta

1½ tablespoons olive oil

1 large onion (preferably Vidalia), diced

1 sweet green pepper, diced

12 medium-size mushrooms, thinly sliced

1 medium-size yellow squash, thinly sliced

¼ cup fat-free Italian dressing

1 large tomato, diced

Parsley sprigs (optional)

❤   ❤   ❤   ❤   ❤

1. In a large pot of boiling, unsalted water, cook pasta according to package directions. Drain.

2. Heat oil in a large skillet set over moderate heat. Add onion and cook 5 minutes. Add pepper, mushrooms, and squash. Cook, stirring frequently until vegetables are tender, 5 to 7 minutes. Add cooked pasta to skillet, pour dressing over and toss to coat. Transfer to a serving bowl and garnish with diced tomato and parsley sprigs if you wish.

Yield: 10 servings

Contributed by:
Dr Keith E. Ellis
Savannah, GA

1 SERVING CONTAINS:

Calories	Fat	Saturated Fat	Cholesterol	Sodium
148	3.3 g	0.5 g	0 mg	51 mg

Skillet Squash

1 tablespoon margarine
1 large onion, diced
5 medium zucchini, sliced ½-inch thick
½ teaspoon salt substitute
¼ teaspoon pepper

❤ ❤ ❤ ❤ ❤

1. Melt margarine in a large skillet over low heat. Add onion and cook, stirring occasionally until softened, about 7 minutes. Add zucchini, toss to coat, reduce heat to low, cover, and cook, stirring occasionally until tender but not mushy, 10 to 15 minutes.

2. Sprinkle with salt substitute and pepper.
   Yield: 5 servings

Contributed by:
Dr Ann L. Holland
Bangor, ME

1 SERVING CONTAINS:

Calories	Fat	Saturated Fat	Cholesterol	Sodium
58	2.4 g	0.4 g	0 mg	35 mg

Jackie's Ratatouille

2 tablespoons olive oil

1 large onion, halved and thinly sliced (1 cup)

3 cloves garlic, minced

3 medium-size zucchini, thinly sliced

1 large red, yellow, or green pepper (or an assortment), diced

5 medium-size tomatoes, chopped

1 bay leaf

1 teaspoon each dried basil and oregano, crumbled

½ teaspoon dried marjoram, crumbled

½ cup plain dried bread crumbs (optional)

1 medium-size eggplant, cubed

❤ ❤ ❤ ❤ ❤

1. Heat oil in a Dutch oven set over moderate heat. Add onion and garlic, cook stirring occasionally until softened, about 7 minutes. Add zucchini, pepper and eggplant, cover and cook 10 minutes, stirring occasionally.

2. Add tomatoes, bay leaf, basil, oregano, and marjoram; cook uncovered, stirring occasionally until vegetables are tender and dish has thickened, 15 to 20 minutes. Remove bay leaf. Add bread crumbs if you'd like an even thicker dish.

3. Serve with crusty french bread.
   Yield: 8 servings

Contributed by:
Dr Phyllis J. Senter
Santa Rosa, CA

1 SERVING CONTAINS:

Calories	Fat	Saturated Fat	Cholesterol	Sodium
113	4.3 g	0.6 g	0 mg	58 mg

Mexican Salad with Salsa Dressing

1 bunch green leaf lettuce, washed, dried, and torn
   into small pieces

1 bunch red leaf lettuce, washed, dried, and torn
   into small pieces

1 cup cilantro leaves

1 cup shredded red cabbage

1 cup thinly sliced red onion

2 medium-size tomatoes, thinly sliced

1 jar (10 ounces) mild, medium, or hot salsa

❤ ❤ ❤ ❤ ❤

1. Combine lettuces, cilantro, cabbage, red onion, and tomatoes in a large
bowl, toss to combine.

2. Add salsa and toss again.
   Yield: **10 servings**

Contributed by:

Dr Brian Graham
Temecula, CA

1 SERVING CONTAINS:

Calories	Fat	Saturated Fat	Cholesterol	Sodium
39	0.4 g	0.1 g	0 mg	314 mg

Curried Vegetables

1 medium head cabbage cut into 1-inch pieces (9 cups)

3 medium all-purpose potatoes, peeled, cut into 1-inch pieces (4 cups)

1 medium-size onion, diced (¾ cup)

3 cloves garlic, minced

6 tablespoons curry powder

½ teaspoon salt

¼ teaspoon ground coriander

¼ teaspoon crushed red chili peppers

1½ cups water

2 cups cooked white rice

½ cup plain low-fat yogurt

♥ ♥ ♥ ♥ ♥

1. Combine cabbage, potatoes, onion, garlic, curry powder, salt, coriander, and chilies in a large saucepan or Dutch oven. Pour water over, stir to combine, and set over moderate heat. Bring to a boil, reduce to a simmer, cover and cook 20 to 25 minutes or until vegetables are tender and almost all the liquid has evaporated.

2. Serve over rice with a dollop of yogurt.
   Yield: 4 servings

Contributed by:
Dr Morris Powell
Bullhead City, AZ

1 SERVING CONTAINS:

Calories	Fat	Saturated Fat	Cholesterol	Sodium
309	2.5 g	0.5 g	2 mg	340 mg

Orzo

¾ cup uncooked orzo (rice shaped pasta)
1 teaspoon olive oil
1 tablespoon minced parsley
1¼ teaspoons grated lemon rind
⅛ teaspoon salt
Freshly ground white pepper to taste

1. Cook orzo in a large pot of boiling (unsalted) water until just tender, following package directions. Drain. Return to cooking pot, add oil, and toss to coat.

2. Add parsley, lemon rind, salt, and pepper, toss again and serve.
   Yield: 2 servings

Contributed by:
Dr Rachel Dawson
Tacoma, WA

1 SERVING CONTAINS:

Calories	Fat	Saturated Fat	Cholesterol	Sodium
212	3.2 g	0.4 g	0 mg	136 mg

Mediterranean Shepherd Salad

2 large cucumbers, peeled, halved lengthwise, seeded, and sliced ½-inch thick

2 medium-size tomatoes, cut into 1-inch dice

1 large sweet green pepper, trimmed and cut into 1 x ½-inch pieces

½ medium-size red onion, cut into 1 x ½-inch pieces

1 large carrot cut into julienne sticks 2 x ¼-inch long

½ cup chopped fresh parsley

1 tablespoon chopped fresh dill

2 tablespoons red wine vinegar

1½ teaspoons canola oil

¼ teaspoon each salt and pepper

❤ ❤ ❤ ❤ ❤

1. In a large bowl combine cucumber, tomato, green pepper, red onion, carrot, parsley, and dill. Sprinkle the vinegar, oil, salt, and pepper and toss well to combine.

2. Chill 1 hour before serving for taste to develop.
   Yield: 4 servings

Contributed by:
Dr Evan Kapp
Austin, TX

1 SERVING CONTAINS:

Calories	Fat	Saturated Fat	Cholesterol	Sodium
77	2.3 g	0.2 g	0 mg	158 mg

Lemon Basil Carrots

1 pound carrots, peeled and sliced
 diagonally in 1-inch pieces
2 tablespoons margarine
1 tablespoon fresh lemon juice
½ teaspoon dried basil, crumbled
Pinch pepper

❤ ❤ ❤ ❤ ❤

1. Cook carrots in a medium-size saucepan of boiling water until just tender, about 12 minutes. Drain. Combine margarine, lemon juice, and basil in saucepan and cook until margarine has melted.

2. Add carrots, sprinkle with pepper, and serve.
 Yield: 6 servings

Contributed by:
Dr William Seidler
Panora, IA

1 SERVING CONTAINS:

Calories	Fat	Saturated Fat	Cholesterol	Sodium
50	2.0 g	0.3 g	0 mg	73 mg

DESSERTS

Boysenberry-Yogurt Sorbet

1 package (16 ounces) frozen, unsweetened
    boysenberries or strawberries

3 tablespoons frozen apple juice concentrate

⅔ cup plain, nonfat yogurt

¼ cup instant, nonfat dry milk

❤ ❤ ❤ ❤ ❤

1. Place half of the berries in the workbowl of a food processor and whirl until blended. Add remaining fruit and apple juice concentrate and puree. Add yogurt and dry milk and whirl until well blended and smooth.

2. Scrape mixture into an 11 x 7-inch baking dish and freeze until almost but not quite solid in the center. Return mixture to the food processor and whirl until creamy. Spoon into individual serving dishes and return to freezer. Remove from freezer 15 minutes before serving.

Yield: **8 servings**

Contributed by:
Dr Brian Graham
Temecula, CA

1 SERVING CONTAINS:

Calories	Fat	Saturated Fat	Cholesterol	Sodium
45	0.2 g	.0 g	1 mg	22 mg

Lemon Cheesecake

Nonstick spray

1 package (3 ounces) diet lemon gelatin dessert

1 cup boiling water

¾ ounce plain melba toast rounds

½ cup skim milk

1 container (16 ounces) nonfat or low-fat cottage cheese

Artificial sweetener to taste

4 strawberries (optional)

♥   ♥   ♥   ♥   ♥

1. Spray a 9-inch pie pan with nonstick spray. Pour gelatin into a 2-cup glass measure, add boiling water, and stir to dissolve. Add enough ice cubes to bring liquid to 12-ounce mark.

2. Dip melba rounds into skim milk, then place rounds in the bottom of the pan. Pour milk and cottage cheese into the workbowl of a food processor and whirl until smooth. Add gelatin mixture and whirl until combined. Carefully pour over melba rounds and chill until set, 2 to 3 hours. Garnish with fresh strawberries if you wish.

Yield: 8 servings

Contributed by:
*Dr Till Bergemann
Greenbelt, MD*

1 SERVING CONTAINS:

Calories	Fat	Saturated Fat	Cholesterol	Sodium
70	1.2 g	0.7 g	5.0 mg	24 mg

Chilled Cherries

1 teaspoon sugar

1 teaspoon flour

¼ cup cold water

½ teaspoon grated lemon rind

⅛ teaspoon ground cinnamon

4 whole cloves

1 can (16 ounces) red, tart pitted cherries in water, drained

½ cup plain low-fat yogurt

4 mint leaves, for garnish

❤ ❤ ❤ ❤ ❤

1. In a small saucepan mix together sugar and flour and stir over low heat for 1 minute. Add water, lemon rind, cinnamon, and cloves, bring to a boil and cook 1 minute. Stir in cherries, remove from heat, and cool. Remove and discard cloves.

2. Stir in yogurt. Spoon into 4 glass bowls, chill, and serve garnished with mint leaves.
   Yield: 4 servings

Contributed by:
Dr Maryann M. Walthier
Garden Grove, CA

1 SERVING CONTAINS:

Calories	Fat	Saturated Fat	Cholesterol	Sodium
73	1.1 g	0.4 g	2 mg	21 mg

Raspberry Sauce

1 package (10 ounces) frozen raspberries, thawed
1 container (8 ounces) plain low-fat yogurt
¼ cup orange juice
1 teaspoon vanilla
Artificial sweetener, to taste

❤ ❤ ❤ ❤ ❤

1. Combine raspberries, yogurt, orange juice, vanilla, and sweetener in a blender or the workbowl of a food processor and whirl until pureed. Push mixture through a fine meshed sieve to remove seeds. Discard seeds.

2. Serve over fresh fruit or angel food cake.
   Yield: 1³/₄ cups (6 servings)

Contributed by:
Dr Michelle May
Phoenix, AZ

1 SERVING CONTAINS:

Calories	Fat	Saturated Fat	Cholesterol	Sodium
52	0.9 g	0.4 g	2 mg	27 mg

Good For You Milkshake

1 large ripe banana, peeled
1 cup (8 ounces) skim milk
1 tablespoon granola
1 teaspoon vanilla

❤   ❤   ❤   ❤   ❤

Combine all ingredients in an electric blender and whirl on high speed until thick and smooth, about 15 seconds.
Yield: **2 servings**

Contributed by:
Dr David West
Grand Junction, CO

1 SERVING CONTAINS:

Calories	Fat	Saturated Fat	Cholesterol	Sodium
118	1.2 g	0.7 g	2 mg	65 mg

Sugar Cookies

Nonstick spray

2 cups all-purpose flour

1½ teaspoons baking powder

1 teaspoon grated lemon rind

½ cup (1 stick) margarine,
  at room temperature

¾ cup granulated sugar

¼ cup firmly packed
  light brown sugar

2 egg whites

2 tablespoons plain low-fat yogurt

1 teaspoon vanilla

2 tablespoons granulated sugar for
  sprinkling

♥ ♥ ♥ ♥ ♥

1. Spray 2 cookie sheets with nonstick spray. Sift together flour and baking powder on a sheet of wax paper.

2. In the large bowl of an electric mixer, cream margarine and sugars until light and fluffy. Beat in the egg whites, yogurt, and vanilla until well combined. Fold in flour mixture. Wrap in plastic wrap and chill several hours.

3. Preheat oven to 375°F. Roll dough out on a lightly floured board to a ¼ inch thickness. Using assorted cookie cutters, cut dough, and place on cookie sheets. Sprinkle with 2 tablespoons of granulated sugar. Bake until crisp and golden around the edges, about 8 minutes.
Yield: **4 dozen 2-inch cookies**

Contributed by:
Dr Andre Weinberger
Washington, DC

1 SERVING CONTAINS:

Calories	Fat	Saturated Fat	Cholesterol	Sodium
55	2.0 g	0.5 g	0 mg	37 mg

Raisin Oatmeal Cookies

Nonstick spray
1 cup old fashioned oats
1½ cups all-purpose flour
½ teaspoon baking soda
½ teaspoon cinnamon
⅛ teaspoon grated nutmeg
2 egg whites

½ cup firmly packed light brown sugar
½ cup granulated sugar
¾ cup vegetable oil
¼ cup skim milk
1 teaspoon vanilla
1 cup raisins

❤ ❤ ❤ ❤ ❤

1. Preheat oven to 350°F. Toast oats in preheated oven until crisp and fragrant, about 10 minutes; set aside. Spray 2 large cookie sheets with nonstick spray.

2. Sift together flour, baking soda, cinnamon, and nutmeg on a sheet of wax paper. In a large bowl, stir together egg whites, sugars, oil, milk, and vanilla. Stir in dry ingredients, oats, and raisins. Drop by rounded teaspoonfuls, 1 inch apart, on cookie sheets. Bake 15 to 18 minutes.
   Yield: **3 dozen cookies**

Contributed by:
*Dr Sharon Gluck
Brooklyn, NY*

1 SERVING CONTAINS:

Calories	Fat	Saturated Fat	Cholesterol	Sodium
80	2.0 g	0.3 g	0 mg	17 mg

Butterscotch Brownies

Nonstick spray
¾ cup unsifted all-purpose flour
1 teaspoon baking powder
Pinch salt
¼ cup vegetable oil

1 cup firmly packed dark brown sugar
2 egg whites
1 teaspoon vanilla
½ cup coarsely chopped pecans

❤ ❤ ❤ ❤ ❤

1. Preheat oven to 350°F. Spray an 8 x 8 x 2-inch baking pan with nonstick cooking spray. Sift together flour, baking powder, and salt on a sheet of wax paper; set aside.

2. In a large bowl, stir together oil, sugar, egg whites, and vanilla. Fold in flour mixture and ¼ cup of the nuts.

3. Spread in prepared pan and sprinkle remaining nuts on top. Bake 30 to 35 minutes or until brownies just begin to pull away from sides of pan. Cool in pan to room temperature. Cut into 32 squares.
Yield: 32 servings

Contributed by:
Dr Andre Weinberger
Washington, DC

1 SERVING CONTAINS:

Calories	Fat	Saturated Fat	Cholesterol	Sodium
65	3.0 g	0.3 g	0 mg	25 mg

White Layer Cake

Nonstick spray

2 cups sifted cake flour

1 teaspoon baking powder

½ teaspoon baking soda

½ cup (1 stick) margarine

1½ cups sugar

4 egg whites

1 cup buttermilk

1 teaspoon vanilla

7-Minute Frosting (recipe below)

❤ ❤ ❤ ❤ ❤

1. Preheat oven to 350°F. Spray two 9-inch layer cake pans with nonstick cooking spray, dust with flour, and line bottom with wax paper rounds.

2. Sift together flour, baking powder, and soda on a sheet of wax paper.

3. In the large bowl of an electric mixer, cream the margarine and 1¼ cups of the sugar until light and fluffy. In a separate bowl, beat egg whites until foamy. Gradually beat in remaining ¼ cup of sugar until stiff peaks form.

4. Alternately fold flour mixture and buttermilk into margarine mixture, beginning and ending with flour mixture. Gently fold in egg whites and vanilla.

5. Spread into prepared pans and bake 30 minutes or until a toothpick inserted in the center comes out clean. Cool on wire rack, then invert and remove from pan. Remove wax paper. Frost with 7-Minute Frosting.

Yield: 16 servings

7-Minute Frosting

2 egg whites

1½ cups sugar

¼ teaspoon cream of tartar

⅓ cup water

1 teaspoon vanilla

1. Combine egg whites, sugar, cream of tartar, and water in the top of a double boiler over simmering water. With an electric mixer, beat on high speed until stiff peaks form, about 7 minutes.

2. Remove from heat, add vanilla, and beat 1 minute longer.

Contributed by:
Dr Sharon Gluck
Brooklyn, NY

1 SERVING CONTAINS:

Calories	Fat	Saturated Fat	Cholesterol	Sodium
251	5.9 g	1.5 g	0 mg	156 mg

Pumpkin Pudding

Nonstick spray

1⅓ cups canned pumpkin

½ cup egg substitute or
    ½ cup egg whites, lightly beaten

4 teaspoons sugar

1 teaspoon vanilla

1½ teaspoons pumpkin pie spice

¾ cup canned evaporated skim milk

¼ cup "light" non-dairy topping (optional)

❤ ❤ ❤ ❤ ❤

1. Preheat oven to 400°F. Spray an 8 x 8-inch baking pan with nonstick spray; set aside.

2. Combine pumpkin, egg, sugar, vanilla, and pumpkin pie spice in the large bowl of an electric mixer and beat 2 minutes on medium speed. Add milk and beat 1 minute longer.

3. Pour into prepared pan and bake 35 minutes or until a toothpick inserted in the center comes out clean. Spoon topping on warm pudding, if you wish.
Yield: **4 servings**

Contributed by:
Dr Judd A. Shafer
Tempe, AZ

1 SERVING CONTAINS:

Calories	Fat	Saturated Fat	Cholesterol	Sodium
85	0.9 g	0.7 g	1 mg	90 mg